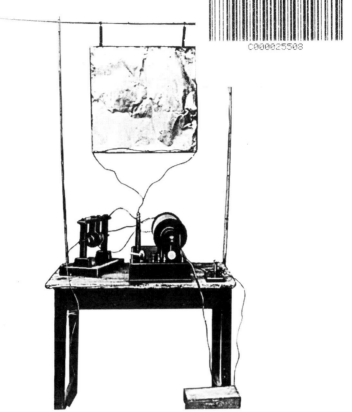

A model of the experimental 1895 spark transmitter with which Marconi tried a new idea of using an elevated aerial and a buried earth in order to improve the transmitting range of his system – a combination which proved vital to the future development of long-distance wireless communication.

OLD RADIO SETS

Jonathan Hill

Shire Publications Ltd

CONTENTS

The pre-broadcasting era 3
The nineteen twenties 8
The nineteen thirties 16
The nineteen forties 21
The nineteen fifties 25
The nineteen sixties 28
Further reading 32
Contacts and useful addresses 32
Places to visit 32

Published in 2003 by Shire Publications Ltd, Cromwell House, Church Street, Princes Risborough, Buckinghamshire HP27 9AA, UK. Website: www.shirebooks.co.uk
Copyright © 1993 by Jonathan Hill. First published 1993; reprinted 1995, 1998, 2001 and 2003. Shire Album 295. ISBN 0 7478 0219 X.

Printed in Great Britain by CIT Printing Services Ltd, Press Buildings, Merlins Bridge, Haverfordwest, Pembrokeshire SA61 1XF.

British Library Cataloguing in Publication Data: Hill, Jonathan. Old Radio Sets. – (Shire Albums; No. 295). I. Title. II. Series. 621.38409. ISBN 0-7478-0219-X.

To Sam and Cavyll.

Cover: *Ekco All-electric Consolette RS3, made by E. K. Cole Ltd in 1931.*

This was the first commercial valve telegraphy receiver to be placed on the market. Made by Marconi's Wireless Telegraph Company in Chelmsford in 1910, the Marconi-Fleming Valve Receiver used two diode detector valves which were designed by Marconi's scientific adviser Sir Ambrose Fleming and put into commercial production by the Edison Swan Electric Company.

Shortly after he arrived in London in February 1896, Marconi was taken to a photographer's portrait studio and, sitting in front of an oilcloth backdrop, posed for this famous photograph with the wireless transmitting and receiving apparatus that he had brought over from Italy laid out on the desk in front of him.

THE PRE-BROADCASTING ERA

Broadcasting as an entertainment and public-service medium started with the formation of the BBC in the early 1920s, and during the same period Britain's domestic wireless-manufacturing industry was set up to supply receivers to an enthusiastic listening public eager to tune in to the new programmes. But long before this, since the late 1890s, wireless communication had been in widespread use throughout the world as wireless *telegraphy* – Morse code sent out over the airwaves by spark transmitters and used mainly for maritime, military and other official purposes.

While Morse telegraphy had been used to communicate overland since the 1840s using wire strung up on poles between sending and receiving stations, it was only towards the end of the Victorian era that the first successful attempts at a working system of wire-less telegraphy were made

by both scientists and amateurs using a Morse key to regulate the discharge of electromagnetic energy by creating a spark and detecting it via an aerial connected to a receiver (diagram 1). Eminent scientists like Edouard Branly, Heinrich Hertz, Oliver Lodge and others from Britain, the United States and France had been experimenting in laboratories in various aspects of electromagnetic waves. But it was a young and untrained Italian, Guglielmo Marconi, who had the foresight to see the significance of these experiments, and who, taking them out of the laboratory and combining them with ideas of his own, developed the world's first practical system of wireless communication.

Seeking to promote and protect his 'invention', Marconi arrived in England in 1896 at the age of 21, bringing with him his wireless transmitting and receiving apparatus, and within a few months filed

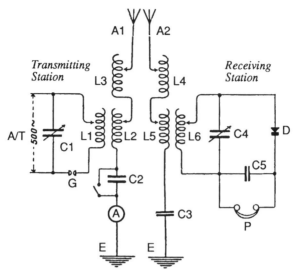

Diagram 1. Spark transmitter and receiver of the pre-broadcast era. Transmitter. Primary circuit A/T, 500 cycle alternator and transformer; C1, variable condenser; G, spark gap; L1, primary coil. Secondary circuit: A1, transmitting aerial; L2, secondary coil; L3, aerial loading coil; C2, condenser; A, aerial ammeter; E, earth. Receiver. Primary circuit: A2, receiving aerial; L4, aerial loading coil; L5, primary coil; C3, condenser; E, earth. Secondary circuit: L6, secondary coil; C4, variable condenser; D, crystal detector; C5, headphone condenser; P, headphones.

Marconi's spark-transmitting room at Poldhu in Cornwall, from which wireless signals were first sent across the Atlantic in December 1901. The spark gap is in front of the window on the right.

4

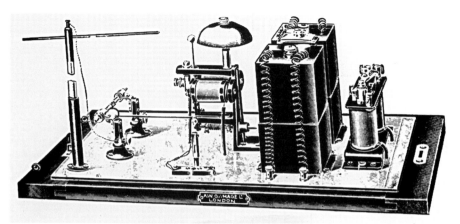

Toy wireless outfit made in Germany in about 1910, giving the young experimenter a chance to transmit Morse code over a distance of about 200 feet (60 metres).

a patent for 'Improvements in transmitting electrical impulses and signals and in apparatus therefore' – the first of its kind in the world.

Initially working closely with the British Post Office, Marconi's first experimental wireless signals travelled only a few miles, but on 12th December 1901, with experience behind him and a system that had reached some sort of perfection, he was able to transmit telegraphy (the Morse letter 'S') to St John's, Newfoundland, from a transmitting station set up at Poldhu in Cornwall, some 1800 miles (2900 km) away. As the demand grew for his system, he formed the Marconi Wireless Telegraph & Signal Company to produce commercial transmitting

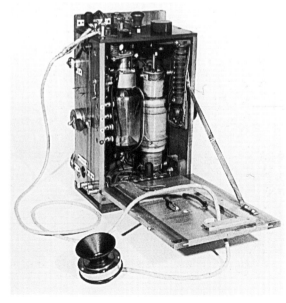

One of the first transmitters to be used by the Royal Flying Corps during the First World War to broadcast the human voice was the Aircraft Telephony Transmitter, adapted in 1915 from a ground set made by Marconi's Wireless Telegraph & Signal Company. It was a single-valve set and was used by spotter aircraft to direct ground fire at enemy positions in the battlefield below.

5

and receiving equipment for coastal land stations and ships at sea, and also for the armed services. During the Edwardian period other wireless companies began to be set up to exploit this new market, which soon included a small but growing number of amateur enthusiasts keen on experimenting. They formed themselves into wireless clubs and made their own wireless transmitters and receivers from component parts or bought complete wireless outfits from firms such as A. W. Gamage Ltd of London. A typical ready-made Gamage's outfit of this period was the 'Atlantic', made by Ward & Goldstone of Manchester. The spark-transmitter unit had a range of about 200 feet (60 metres) and comprised a condenser, a spark gap, a Morse key and an 8 foot (2.4 metre) extending aerial. The same type of aerial was fitted to the receiver unit, which used a 'coherer' type of wireless detector. Priced at £6, this outfit represented about a month's good wages, but one of the delights of owning it included being able to listen for the first time to the new Morse time signals sent from the Eiffel Tower transmitting station in Paris, which enabled the ordinary person to set his watch and clocks accurately.

Although a few experiments had been conducted into the transmission of speech (wireless *telephony*), notably R. A. Fessenden's attempts in 1906 to broadcast programmes of music and speech at Brant Rock, Massachusetts, this was not practicable with the equipment and technology then available, until the development of the valve. The valve was pioneered by Lodge's detector diode of 1904 and Langmuir's triode amplifier of 1907, but it was not until the First World War that it was perfected, and spark transmitters continued to dominate the airwaves up to 1914.

During the war there was an urgent need to supply the allied armies with wireless equipment and also to do research into improving existing equipment. One of the greatest developments of this time was an amplifying valve known as the French, or 'R' valve. By 1917 this valve was in general use in telephony receivers and transmitters allowing spoken instructions to be communicated, where before these had been sent by Morse.

Immediately after the war, the Marconi Company began experimenting with high-power telephony transmitters and in 1919 succeeded in transmitting the voice of their engineer, W. T. Ditcham, across the Atlantic. Other wireless-equipment manu-

This beautifully made crystal set was widely used by Royal Flying Corps ground stations during the First World War to receive wireless telegraphy signals covering the 100/700 metre wave-range. Made by the Automatic Telephone Manufacturing Company in 1916, the Mark III Short Wave Tuner appeared again after the war when hundreds of surplus sets were eagerly bought up and adapted to receive the new BBC stations when broadcasting began in November 1922.

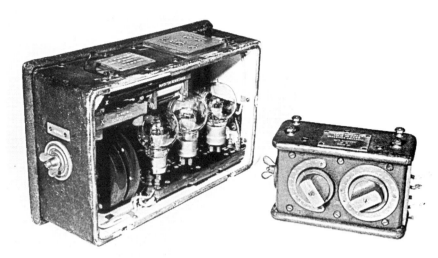

Aircraft Receiver Mark III (left), manufactured by the Automatic Telephone Manufacturing Company in 1917 – a three-valve telephony receiver using 'R' valves fitted as standard in British aircraft in the closing months of the First World War. The matching remote-control tuner unit (right) – Tuner Aircraft Mark III (Receiver Control).

facturers in England, such as the Radio Communications Company in Slough, soon began setting up experimental wireless telephony stations and had the idea of manufacturing wireless receivers so that ordinary people could listen to their transmissions. So a separate domestic wireless-manufacturing industry began to emerge which, in anticipation of future broadcasting developments, concentrated on making receivers specifically for home entertainment and not for any military or professional use.

Early in 1920 the several thousand amateur wireless enthusiasts already had a fairly good choice of wireless telephony stations to tune into, although their programmes were rather sporadic and at times unannounced: music from station PCGG in The Hague, Holland (known to English listeners as 'the Dutch Concerts'), programmes of news, talks and music broadcast from Marconi's works at Chelmsford, and from amateur telephony transmitting stations around Britain. On 15th June 1920 the famous opera singer Dame Nellie Melba gave a special concert from Chelmsford which captured listeners' imagination and firmly established the idea of wireless as an entertainment.

Interest in wireless continued to grow and on 18th October 1922 the British Broadcasting Company was formed. This was, in essence, a commercial company comprising some three hundred British manufacturers and dealers in wireless equipment who produced receivers and accessories and provided the broadcast programmes. They were headed by the so-called 'Big Six': British Thomson-Houston Company Ltd, the General Electric Company Ltd, Marconi's Wireless Telegraph Company Ltd, Metropolitan-Vickers Electrical Company Ltd, the Radio Communication Company Ltd, and the Western Electric Company Ltd. The BBC's first local station, call-sign 2LO, opened in London on Tuesday 14th November 1922, transmitting on the medium waveband to an audience of just 18,000 who had taken out the new 10 shilling Broadcast Receiving Licence. Broadcasting had begun!

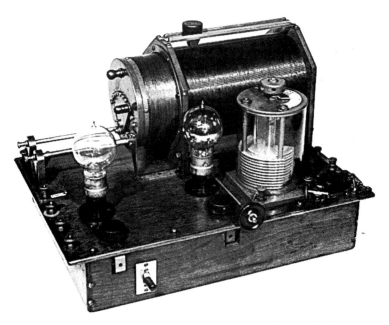

Although not of commercial manufacture, this home-constructed two-valve battery-powered receiver is of the highest quality. It was lovingly made by an amateur listener in about 1920.

THE NINETEEN TWENTIES

Within a few weeks of 2LO coming on the air, other BBC transmitters had opened in Birmingham, Manchester and Newcastle upon Tyne, and some 35,000 receiving licences had been issued. Each transmitter was of relatively low power and was designed to serve its immediate local area only. The simplest form of receiver was a crystal set (diagram 2), which used a mineral crystal, commonly galena, as a detector. The received signals were unamplified by the crystal set and, while fairly weak, could be picked up if the set was used within about a 10 mile (16 km) radius of a transmitting station. Like today's Walkman, the crystal set was designed for personal listening through a single pair of headphones only and, without the additional expense of purchasing an amplifier, it would not work with a loudspeaker. But there was a cheaper,

tried and tested method of amplification available: placing the headphones inside a deep fruit bowl did seem to make the sound louder!

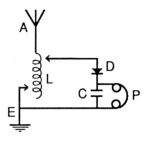

Diagram 2. Simple crystal set of the early 1920s: A, aerial; C, variable condenser; D, crystal detector; L, tuning coil; E, earth; P, headphones.

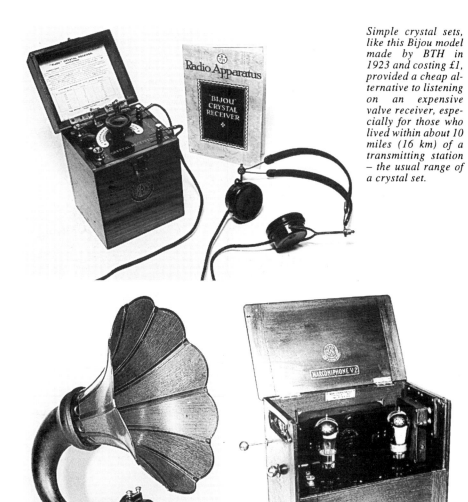

Simple crystal sets, like this Bijou model made by BTH in 1923 and costing £1, provided a cheap alternative to listening on an expensive valve receiver, especially for those who lived within about 10 miles (16 km) of a transmitting station – the usual range of a crystal set.

Left: *The development of loudspeakers coincided with the development of valve receivers powerful enough to drive them. The Type AR19, Standard Dragon, was a horn loudspeaker with a beautifully made petal-design flare constructed from sectioned oak. It was made by Graham Amplion Ltd in 1923 and, as with all loudspeakers, enabled the whole family to listen rather than just a solitary person with headphones.*

Right: *The Marconiphone V2 was one of the growing number of commercially manufactured domestic wireless receivers available on the market when the BBC first began broadcasting in November 1922. Its production was a joint venture between Marconi's Wireless Telegraph Company and Plessey, who made the chassis. Costing £25, it was a two-valve battery-powered receiver designed for headphone use and could tune from 185 to 3200 metres.*

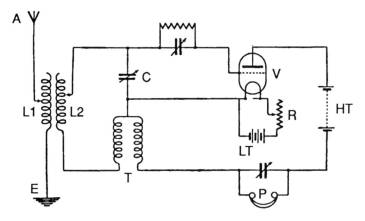

Diagram 3. Simple battery valve receiver of the early 1920s: A, aerial; C, variable condenser; L1, tuning inductance (primary); L2, tuning inductance (secondary); T, RF transformer; V, valve; R, filament resistor; HT, high-tension battery; LT, low-tension battery; P, headphones; E, earth.

For those who could afford it, a battery valve receiver (diagram 3) improved the sound quality and could drive a loudspeaker, thus making it possible for the whole family to gather round and listen together. Batteries (known as 'accumulators') had to be recharged about once a fortnight; the local garage could usually do this at 6d a time, and demand for this service was such that many enterprising garage owners began battery rounds. Listeners were spoilt for choice with over five hundred different models available, ranging from the cheapest crystal set at 7s 6d to a top-range multi-valve receiver at £65 or more. Both types of receiver needed to be connected to an outdoor aerial (diagram 4), usually a large cumbersome structure using 100 feet (30 metres) of wire strung up between two masts, or hung from a convenient chimney or tree, with another wire going from the earth terminal of the set and making a good connection with the ground. In all, hundreds of feet of wire were used in the aerial, earth, component connections, tuning coils and so on – which led to a number of music-hall jokes about it being a wire*less* hobby! Alongside commercially manufactured receivers, there was a tremendous interest in home construction, making receivers from scratch, from kits or from plans printed in the various wireless magazines such as *Wireless World* and *Popular Wireless*.

At this time in the development of wire-

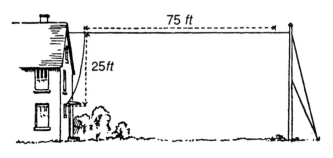

Diagram 4. An outdoor aerial set-up of the early 1920s.

The panel of this five-valve battery-powered receiver made by W. R. H. Tingey early in 1922 is smothered in controls – thirteen knobs, five switches and fourteen terminals – years before the days of single-knob tuning! Dials were calibrated in degrees, and the settings of each control for each broadcasting station had to be carefully noted and logged.

less it was most unusual for station names to appear on tuning dials. Stations moved wavelengths fairly frequently and there was always a new one somewhere coming on the air for the first time. Tuning controls were marked in degrees, and each control setting of each particular station had to be carefully noted down in a log for future reference.

The BBC's policy of installing several low-power medium-wave transmitting stations around Britain continued, until by the end of 1924 some 21 had opened. However, during that year the idea had developed of serving the entire country by a single high-power long-wave station to carry a national programme to supplement listeners' local stations. To test the idea, an experimental transmitter was erected at Chelmsford. After a series of successful experimental broadcasts from there, the station was transferred to a permanent, centrally located site at Daventry in Northamptonshire and on Monday 27th July 1925 it opened on 1600 metres long-wave, using the call-sign 5XX. An editorial in the *Radio Times* estimated that one million listeners could pick up the new station on a crystal set in most parts of Britain, and now for the first time listeners had a choice of either their own medium-wave local station programme or one of a more national character from 5XX. (Further investigation proved that the range of 5XX was not sufficient to serve

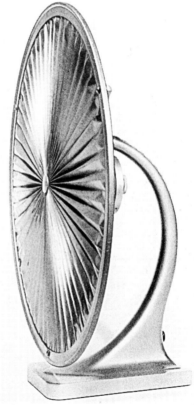

Sterling Primax, an early moving-iron loudspeaker with a painted Lumière paper diaphragm and cast-aluminium frame and stand. Manufactured by the Sterling Telephone & Electric Company in 1924.

11

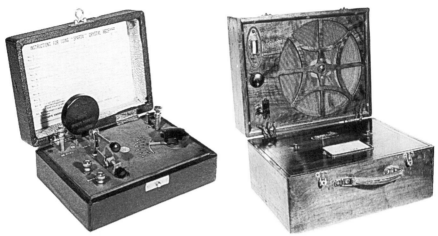

Left: *The Sparta Crystal Set, manufactured by Fullers United Electric Works in July 1924, tuned to the 300/500 metre medium waveband and, by means of a plug-in tuning coil, to the BBC's new long-wave experimental station at Chelmsford on 1600 metres which opened that year.*

Right: *The Chakophone Junior Four 'suitcase' battery portable, made by the Eagle Engineering Company in 1929. The suitcase-type walnut cabinet housed a four-valve receiver together with its associated batteries, frame aerial and moving-iron cone loudspeaker. So completely self-contained was it that, not only could it be used in any room of the house, but also it could be taken on picnics or on motor outings.*

Left: *A quality four-valve battery receiver, Model TM2, Type F6, manufactured in 1925 by A. J. Stevens & Company. Various wave-ranges could be selected by inserting the appropriate plug-in tuning coils. After use, the lid of the inlaid mahogany cabinet could be closed and locked.*

Right: *Baby Grand, AC Mains Model, made by Gambrell Brothers Ltd in August 1926. By the second half of the 1920s developments in circuit technology had enabled the successful introduction of plug-in mains receivers which by the end of the 1930s had ousted the battery-powered model. The Baby Grand was the first valve wireless receiver to be produced in Britain which entirely dispensed with batteries.*

The Special Effects Department of the BBC in London, 1927 – most essential for creating the right atmosphere in a radio play, etc. (Photograph: courtesy of the BBC.)

the whole country and so in time a number of National Programme relay stations using the medium waveband were built to extend coverage.)

Brownie Two-Valve Receiver, manufactured by the Brownie Wireless Company (of Great Britain) Ltd in 1927. Announced as 'a valve set for the million', this cheap and basic two-valve battery-powered receiver represented a disappearing type of design with its externally mounted valves and tuning coils.

The popularity of crystal sets though, had now begun to wain and sales of battery valve receivers, with their better sound quality and loudspeaker reception, began to increase. Interest began in outdoor battery portables which housed all the essential parts (aerial, receiver, batteries and loudspeaker) within a suitcase type of cabinet, which, being entirely self-contained, was ideal for taking on outings, picnics and so on.

In 1926 an important development occurred with the introduction of the first AC mains-operated receiver, the Gambrell Baby Grand. The mains electricity supply to private homes at this time was chaotic, with several hundred small, locally based electricity companies using a variety of non-standard voltages in both AC and DC. Millions of older houses, particularly those in rural areas, were not connected to the mains but for those that were the mains receiver was to be a considerable advance for it dispensed with

13

The number of controls is diminishing, and the valves and other components are now mostly hidden within the wireless cabinet. The battery-powered Burndept Screened Four, made by Burndept Wireless Ltd in January 1928, reflected a design trend which would soon become universal throughout the wireless-manufacturing industry.

the need for batteries and the great inconvenience of having them charged. By the mid 1930s mains receivers were universal, partly as a result of the building of the National Grid high-tension mains transmission system across Britain and the setting up of the Central Electricity Board which consolidated the various electricity companies under a single national body

and standardised the supply.

The first public airing of the Gambrell Baby Grand was at a new national wireless exhibition at Olympia in London, held from 4th to 18th September 1926. Soon known as 'Radiolympia', this show immediately established itself as the venue for wireless manufacturers to launch their latest models and as the traditional beginning of 'the wireless season'. One notable design trend seen at the first Radiolympia was the overall simplification of controls exhibited on most receivers – compare the Gambrell with the 1922 Tingey five-valve receiver (see page 11).

On 1st January 1927 the British Broadcasting Corporation was created by Royal Charter. The new BBC took over from the original British Broadcasting Company, acquiring its staff, studios and transmitters and paying off its old commercial shareholders. Its first Director-General was John Reith who saw to it that the BBC's already established policy of political independence and impartiality

McMichael Colonial Receiver, made by L. McMichael Ltd in 1931. This four-valve battery-powered receiver is housed in an insect-proof teak cabinet, for its primary use was out in the British colonies in readiness for the BBC's new short-wave Empire Service. The novel tuning unit on the left of the control panel was turned around to select one of three short-wave ranges and, for use in Britain, the broadcast band on the medium-wave.

A stylish AC mains valve receiver, Gecophone All Electric Three Valve Receiver, Model BC 3130, made by the General Electric Company in 1930. The black-painted wooden cabinet has been sprayed with gold lacquer and is offset by a gilded metal escutcheon surrounding the twin tuning scales.

and that of providing a public service were carried out to the letter.

More broadcasting schemes took shape towards the end of the 1920s. While the National Programme from 5XX continued, a 'sister' high-power medium-wave transmitter at Daventry (call-sign 5GB) was brought into service on 27th August 1927 to carry out experimental broadcasts to the Midlands region. Together 5GB and 5XX made up the world's first twin-wave transmitting station and were the forerunners of the Regional Scheme in which each transmitting station had two separate and independent transmitters radiating different and contrasting national and regional programmes.

Transmissions also began that year from an experimental short-wave station at Chelmsford (call-sign G5SW) set up to test the viability of a broadcasting service to the far-off British colonies and dominions. As these tests could also be picked up at home, several manufacturers started to produce short-wave only receivers and by the time regular short-wave broadcasting began in 1932 (with the BBC's Empire Service), this part of the industry was already well established.

By the end of the 1920s, when nearly three million Broadcast Receiving Licences had been issued, the two types of receiver which had established the British wireless industry just a few years before – the crystal set and the battery valve receiver with its separate batteries and external loudspeaker – had become obsolete and the mains receiver and the outdoor battery portable with everything self-contained within an attractive cabinet would predominate right through the 1930s and beyond.

Left: *Pye Model K, a two-valve AC mains receiver with a built-in loudspeaker made by Pye Radio Ltd in 1932. This was one of a range of Pye models whose Art Deco 'sunrise' loudspeaker grilles graced wireless-set designs from 1927 to 1948.*
Right: *A classic wireless set from the 1930s, the Philips Model 634A, made by Philips Lamps Ltd in 1933. This five-valve AC mains receiver is housed in a very elegant mahogany cabinet with a moulded Bakelite loudspeaker and dial surround; station names and settings are printed on a pull-out card slotted beneath the set. Following its appearance in the nostalgic Ovaltine advertisements on television in the early 1980s, collectors named the 634A 'the Ovaltiney set'.*

THE NINETEEN THIRTIES

The spread of the National Grid system in the early part of the 1930s, bringing mains electricity into tens of thousands of individual homes and included as standard in the new suburban housing estates being built throughout Britain, helped to firmly establish the mains-powered receiver, which soon evolved into the piece of wood furniture people called 'the wireless'.

As a material, wood was strong and often beautifully grained. It was easy to cut and assemble into a box shape and was therefore highly suitable for making not only wireless cabinets but also the cabinets of a new sector of the industry – radiograms. Following the introduction of electric gramophone pickups and turntables in 1928, many leading wireless manufacturers had begun by the early 1930s to produce impressive floor-standing radiogram versions of their principal wireless receiver models. These console radiograms, epitomised by their often magnificent and monolithic mahogany or walnut cabinets housing mains radio, electric turntable with autochanger and perhaps several large loudspeakers, soon displaced the old wind-up gramophone from the living rooms of the nation's rich and became one of the great status symbols of the 1930s – a favourite retirement present for company directors!

For those listeners not able to afford a radiogram, almost all wireless sets now came with 'gramophone' terminals at the back. To these could be connected an add-on electric turntable or simply an ordinary wind-up gramophone fitted with an electric pickup, making use of the receiver's circuit as an auxiliary amplifier.

Besides wood, there was now another material being used in the wireless cabinet-making industry: the phenolic plastic Bakelite. While it had been used to make

The imposing RGD Model 880 all-wave radiogram, made by the Radio Gramophone Development Company in 1937, seems particularly at home in its panelled mock-Tudor drawing room. Priced at £84, these 'aristocrats of the radio world' were only for the well-off.

The BBC's Chief Announcer, Stuart Hibberd, at the microphone on 22nd February 1934. His was one of the most famous and best-loved voices on vintage BBC radio – warm, dependable, courteous and dignified. At the end of the day, his closing announcements over the air always ended with a sincere 'Goodnight everybody . . . . Goodnight' which gave the impression that he was speaking personally to those listening at home. The pause, he explained, was designed to give listeners a chance of saying 'Goodnight' back to him. (Photograph: courtesy of the BBC.)

a few wireless cabinets since the end of the 1920s, it was only during the 1930s that Bakelite came into its own in this field and, lending itself perfectly to mass-production techniques, it became the favourite among many wireless manufacturers, especially E. K. Cole Ltd, who exploited its fine moulding properties and sometimes produced exciting and innovative design shapes.

By the mid 1930s listening to the wireless had become more of an international activity, with receivers capable of tuning into most, if not all, of the two hundred or so broadcasting stations now scattered around Europe. Apart from the BBC's own stations sending out the national and regional programmes, broadcasts in the English language could also be received from foreign commercial stations such as Radio Normandie (Fécamp) and Radio Luxembourg, which interspersed their light entertainment shows with advertisements for stockings, cigarettes and so on, or tried to persuade parents to give their children Ovaltine before they went to bed!

With so many stations on the air

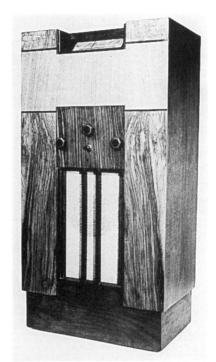

Ferranti Arcadia Console made by Ferranti Ltd in 1935. This floor-standing five-valve receiver is housed in a most beautiful rosewood- and walnut-veneered cabinet with a simulated mother-of-pearl tuning scale.

Ekco Model AD65, made by E. K. Cole Ltd in 1934. Designed by the architect Wells Coates, this was the first in a range of 'round Ekcos' in moulded Bakelite cabinets produced until 1946. The design was no more than novel at the time, but today it has almost achieved cult status amongst certain over-enthusiastic wireless collectors and antique dealers.

(including from 1936 the BBC's new television service from Alexandra Palace, the sound from which could be picked up by some wireless receivers of this time), accurate tuning became very important. To find a station, listeners no longer had to refer to a station log and then find the correct setting for the controls as they had done in the 1920s, for most wireless sets had dials fully marked with station names and the listener simply had to move the tuning pointer to the appropriate station. As an aid to tuning, visual tuning indicators started to become a feature of many new sets: chief among these was the magic-eye tuning indicator, which was able to show visually and with pinpoint accuracy when the required station was fully tuned in.

Another tuning innovation occurred in

Left: *Pilot Model U650. Pilot Radio Ltd made this six-valve receiver in 1936 and it was one of the first sets on the market to incorporate a magic-eye tuning indicator.*

Right: *Philco Model V537, made in 1937 by Philco Radio & Television Corporation Ltd. Housed in a moulded Bakelite cabinet, this receiver was one in a cheap Philco range of 'People's Sets', designed for mass appeal.*

The Ferranti Model 139, made by Ferranti Ltd in 1939 and housed in a brown moulded Bakelite cabinet. (Model 239 was the wooden cabinet version of the same set.)

Push-button tuning made changing stations more convenient for listeners in the late 1930s, with up-to-the-minute receivers like this Bush Model PB 51 of 1938.

1938, when push-button tuning became very popular with receiver manufacturers for the first time. Pre-tuned by the wireless retailer or by the customer himself when he got home, several favourite stations could be selected literally at the push of a button, which made tuning much easier than manually searching for the right station. More sophisticated methods employed small electric motors which swept the pointer around the dial in either direction. There were a few technical problems with some of the push-button mechanisms, particularly on some of the cheaper sets, but in general they were liked by the public and became the fashionable type of set to buy.

As the decade drew to a close, it seemed likely that Britain was once again heading for war with Germany. This was reflected by some wireless manufacturers who in the summer of 1939 were targeting the seasonal interest in outdoor battery portables at Air Raid Precautions officials and owners of air-raid shelters, whom *The Wireless and Electrical Trader*

thought of as good prospects for sales. Radiolympia opened as usual and everyone was looking forward to the expected autumn sales boom when on 1st September Germany invaded Poland. With blackout regulations coming into force and civilian evacuation plans getting under way, the show was forced to close prematurely. On the same day the BBC made immediate changes to its wavelength and service structure, introducing at 8.15 in the evening a single combined programme on the medium waveband, with all its transmitters synchronised to radiate the same wavelength – a move designed to prevent enemy aircraft from using the transmitters as navigation beacons.

Two days later there was one of the most memorable broadcasts in wireless history, when at 11.15 am on Sunday 3rd September millions of listeners heard the Prime Minister, Neville Chamberlain, make the grave announcement that a state of war existed between Great Britain and Germany.

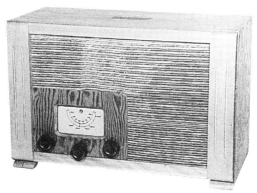

The rarer version of the Wartime Civilian Receiver ('Utility Set'), the 1944 battery model. Housed in a plain and austere-looking pinewood cabinet, both the battery model and the more common mains version were produced by the combined effort of over forty wireless-set manufacturers, whose brief was to produce a cheap and basic receiver of standard design to counter the severe shortages caused by the demands of war on the domestic wireless industry.

THE NINETEEN FORTIES

On 7th January 1940 the BBC's Forces Programme was introduced on the medium waveband primarily to serve the British Expeditionary Force in northern France with morale-boosting light entertainment. At home, with more and more wireless factories switching to essential war work, the domestic wireless-manufacturing industry all but came to a halt. Very few new sets appeared on the market and supplies of valves, batteries and other components useful for keeping existing sets going were severely curtailed. By 1942 thousands of sets were awaiting repair simply because either spares or repair men (drafted into the forces) were unavailable. Some help came from the United States, which sent shipments of valves and receivers, but the British government decided to ask the British wireless industry to produce a cheap standard receiver. Known as the 'Utility Set', this became available in 1944 in both mains and battery versions and ensured that the public were at least kept informed and entertained.

Very soon after the war had ended in 1945, the first receivers began coming off the production line as manufacturers gradually began to get back to peacetime production. The structure of the wireless industry, its technology and production methods had changed dramatically since 1939, when it was principally concerned with producing relatively simple wireless

The first post-war set to appear on the market – the Ferranti Model 145, housed in a Bakelite cabinet of pre-war appearance.

Left: *The Murphy Model AD 94 was the first Murphy receiver to be housed in an all-Bakelite cabinet. Since the early 1930s the company had used wood in a variety of rather bizarre cabinet styles. Made in 1940, the AD 94 tuned to the short and long wavebands and used a five-valve circuit. Its cabinet (designed by Eden Minns) was later also used to house the 1945 Murphy models SAD 94S and SAD 94L.*

Right: *The Rees-Mace Type RMC battery receiver was one of 125,000 domestic receivers held up in the production line at the beginning of the war because of component shortages. It was finally released in April 1943.*

receivers for people's homes. Following wartime research and development, it was now also skilled and equipped in the modern and intricate technology of electronic engineering and had earned the modern title of the 'Radio' industry – the word 'wireless', in professional and official circles at least, was thought of as being rather archaic and inappropriate.

On 29th July 1945 the BBC introduced the new Light Programme on 1500 metres long-wave. It was immediately popular, providing a combination of light music, comedy and light drama interspersed with regular news summaries. This was followed in September 1946 by an entirely new type of programme 'for

A rather romantic illustration of wireless -set production as war clouds gather in 1939. Getting ready for the expected autumn sales boom, valiant-looking British workers carry out tests on chassis held in protective cradles, while above them finished chassis relentlessly pass by on an overhead conveyor.

Left: *The five-valve Bush Model AC 91 is a small compact receiver aimed at the 'second set' market and designed for the kitchen or bedroom. Made in 1946 it covers the short, medium and long wavebands and is similar in appearance to the Bush Model DAC 90 (1946) and the Bush Model DAC 90A (1950).*
Right: *The design influences of the 1930s are still evident in this 1947 five-valve push-button receiver by GEC, the Model BC 4750, housed in a mahogany-veneered plywood cabinet and tuning to the short, medium and long wavebands.*

the alert and receptive listener' – the Third Programme. With the Home Service, these two programmes became the mainstay of the BBC's radio network until 1967.

One of the new type of sets to emerge soon after the war was known as the 'second set'. These were small compact radios which were ideal for placing in a kitchen or bedroom to supplement the 'house' radio, which was usually kept in the lounge. The neat size of many new receivers produced after 1945 was a direct result of the miniaturisation of circuitry. In particular, the introduction of the all-glass miniature valve, developed in the United States during the war and quickly introduced into British

sets as the B7G, helped reduce the size of chassis needed in both mains and portable sets.

On 1st October 1947 the first post-war National Radio Exhibition opened at Olympia and did much to re-establish the prestige of the British radio industry, with over 170 principal exhibitors showing an impressive line-up of radios and electronics to an audience starved of a national radio show since 1939. Among new developments, many sets had 'fly-wheel' tuning, in which a heavy fly-wheel was fitted to the shaft of the tuning control knob; if this was spun, the inertia of the fly-wheel then carried it on. This made it quick and easy to pass from one end of the tuning scale to the other, but this innovation only lasted a season or two!

In the United States the world's first component transistor (the 'point-contact transfer resistor') was developed at Bell Telephone Laboratories by John Bardeen and Walter Brattain. Describing it as an 'amplifying crystal', *Wireless World* thought that 'the transistor could usefully take the place of valves' – a prophecy which came true by the mid 1960s.

Model 1117. With twin loudspeakers and treble and bass tone controls, sound quality was the selling point of this 1948 HMV receiver.

Richard Murdoch and Kenneth Horne at the microphone in 1948, broadcasting their successful comedy series on the BBC, 'Much-Binding-in-the-Marsh'. (Photograph: courtesy of the BBC.)

This unusual short-wave battery set made by Ever-Ready in 1948 was called the 'Saucepan Special' because its blue-sprayed metal case was made by a north London saucepan factory. Principally designed for the central African market, it sat on its own 300-hour battery, which was too big to fit inside!

Left: *The Ekco Model A147 of 1951 had no tuning knob as such, but was pre-set by the radio retailer to four stations of the listener's choice, and these could then be selected by means of a simple switch. Brought out to co-incide with the Festival of Britain celebrations, the Model A147 was also known as the Festival.*

Right: *This small four-valve mains receiver is another example of the 'second-set' type. Made by Champion Electric Corporation Ltd in 1952, the Model TRF 784 was attractively housed in a moulded cream-coloured plastic case less than 12 inches (30 cm) long.*

THE NINETEEN FIFTIES

In the spring of 1950 the BBC began occasional VHF (very high frequency) test broadcasts from Wrotham in Kent and these eventually led to the inauguration of their first regular high-power VHF/FM (frequency modulation) service on 2nd May 1955. This instantly gave impetus to the creation of a new market in VHF/FM receivers, tuners and radiograms, bought mainly by hi-fi enthusiasts seeking better-quality broadcast listening.

Radiograms had enjoyed popularity since appearing in the early 1930s, and now the market was given a boost by the introduction of the first 33⅓ rpm (revolutions per minute) microgroove long-playing record, which gave greater playing time and better sound quality compared with scratchy old 78s.

To mark the coronation of Queen Elizabeth II, Ultra Electric Ltd brought out their Coronation Twin (Model R786) mains/battery portable in 1953. Housed in a plum-coloured plastic case with a cream Perspex front, it is considered among the most stylish portables to be produced in post-war years, although its 'de-luxe' version, model R906, with its case covered with simulated crocodile skin, was thought to outshine it at the time!

Radiograms continued to be impressive throughout the 1950s and 1960s, but from the early 1970s fashions and public taste changed and there was no longer a call for such grand and opulent pieces of furniture. For the hi-fi enthusiast and 'novice' listener alike there were 'audio separates' (stereo systems built up of separately housed units), and for teenagers and students, compact 'music centres' (comprising a stereo radio, record player and cassette tape deck mounted on a wood plinth under a smoked perspex cover, with little loudspeakers which could fit tidily on a bedsit bookshelf).

Vidor's 'Lady Margaret' battery portable of 1954 is typical of the type of receiver principally aimed at the female market in the early to mid 1950s. Housed in a scarlet and silver-grey 'lizard-skin' covered wooden case, this was one of a growing number of sets available (according to Vidor's 1954 sales brochure) 'in feminine colours, and no larger than a lady's handbag'. The lid houses a frame aerial although by this time miniature ferrite-rod aerials were being introduced – raising and lowering the lid switches the set on and off.

Apart from the occasional acknowledgement to female listeners in the past (notably a pair of ladies' headphones brought out by Sterling in 1922), the radio industry had largely ignored women as potential customers. However, that changed in the early 1950s with a flood of receivers specifically designed for and aimed at the female buyer. These sets were invariably petite, pastel in colour and often resembled a ladies' handbag, and they bore such non-aggressive names as 'Sky Princess' and 'Lady Margaret'. This attention lasted only a few years until the industry turned to another lucrative market – teenagers. As has already been seen, the BBC had been founded in 1922 by over three hundred different radio-related manufacturing companies. By the mid 1950s there started a great movement towards merg-

Perhaps the most important British set of more modern times, the Pam Model 710, the first British all-transistor radio to be placed on the market. Made by Pam (Radio & Television) Ltd in June 1956, the 710 used an eight-transistor printed circuit covering the medium waveband and the Light Programme on 1500 metres longwave.

ers and takeovers, with many established smaller companies like Cossor and McMichael being progressively taken over by larger ones until by 1962, five major groups dominated the industry (see next chapter).

Following the development of component transistors in the United States, they had begun to be employed in electronic circuits by the mid 1950s. Their introduction heralded the era of true miniaturisation, high reliability and low power consumption, and they were soon applied to every field of electronics, eventually displacing the valve which had reigned supreme for several decades. Beaten by the Americans by two years and by the Japanese by one year, the first British transistor radio to come on the market was the 1956 Pam Model 710. Although designed at Pye Ltd's research laboratories at Cambridge, the 710 was released through a Pye subsidiary, Pam Radio & Television Ltd, because the parent company was uncertain of the radio's commercial viability and was unwilling to risk its own reputation on such an untried innovation. Priced at £31 10s 1d, it was an expensive investment for the listening public, but sufficient numbers were sold and well received for Pye to bring out its own modified version (Model 123BQ) early the following year. Several other manufacturers now began gingerly to enter this new field, but only one, Perdio, decided to specialise in producing tran-

Left: *The HMV Model 1410G battery portable of 1957: an interesting hybrid receiver marking the changeover from valves to transistors with its three-valve/two-transistor circuit.*
Right: *Although this transistor portable appears to be a British receiver, being very similar in style to the 1956 Pam model 710 (see previous page), it is an early Japanese attempt to enter the European market by producing a receiver imitating western design. Made by Tokyo Tsushin Kogyo Ltd in 1957, the design of Model TR72 was not repeated, for in January of the following year TTK Ltd changed its name to the Sony Corporation, since when, relying upon their own design ideas, the company has flourished.*

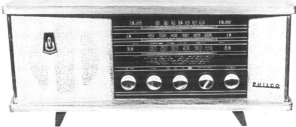

The Philco Model 100 of 1958 – an AM/FM mains valve receiver housed in a very stylish cabinet on little tapered wooden legs. This style of cabinet was known in the trade as 'the long, low look' and is typical of many table-model receivers of the late 1950s and early 1960s.

sistor sets to the exclusion of all other types of receiver.

At this stage in its development, the component transistor was still generally incapable of equalling valve performance, especially at high frequencies, and was ideally suitable only for handling relatively low powers. Because of this, some transistor radios of this period were hybrids, with valves in the HF and IF stages, and transistors only in the output stages.

In the mains class of receiver, a new style appeared with the 'long, low look', epitomised in the design of the Philco Model 100 with its horizontal wooden case

perched on little tapered legs.

As the new decade approached, public interest in transistor portables continued to grow and, with mass-production getting under way, their overall cost gradually dropped and this new area of radio boosted sales, especially in the summer months. However, at the same time a few small pocket-size transistor radios were beginning to be imported into Britain from the Far East. The trickle became a flood which continued well into the 1960s and eventually all but killed off the British radio industry.

An Ekco Model PT352 'pocket' transistor and one of its smaller Japanese rivals, the New Voice Transistor 6, both 1961. The Japanese were by now beginning to make a concerted attack on the British portable-radio market and within a few years only a few British manufacturers, including Roberts Radio, who are still going today, would be producing British-made radio sets.

THE NINETEEN SIXTIES

By 1960, about 70 per cent of British households had a television receiver and until then sales were accounting for four-fifths of the industry's turnover. Manufacturers had invested heavily in this expanding area throughout the 1950s while the BBC and, after 1955, the new ITV television service spread across the country. But, with the television market now approaching saturation point, the industry fell into a general slump and many firms found themselves in financial difficulty, not helped by growing imports of cheap, pocket-size transistor radios from Japan and Hong Kong. These little sets were immediately appealing to the buying public (especially to the new 'pop generation' of teenagers), not only because of their handy size, styling and comparative cheapness, but also because they exhibited new and attractive packaging ideas and usually came with several individually wrapped accessories such as an earpiece, batteries and a carrying case, all contained in a tempting presentation box. By 1961, in which year over 160 different transistor models were released on to the market, every portable radio was a transistor, with very few exceptions; one of the very last valve portables to be manufactured was the Ever Ready 'Sky Captain'.

In comparison to their Far Eastern rivals, British-made transistor radios were larger and, without the advantage of cheap labour and components, were generally more expensive to produce. Faced with this competition and with the slump in sales, and having overstretched themselves in television investment, several companies, large and small, including Perdio, went out of business or were taken over by one of the five major groups: British Electronic Industries Ltd, Rank Bush Murphy, GEC/Radio & Allied Industries Ltd, Philips Electrical Ltd and Thorn Electrical Industries Ltd.

By the mid 1960s most British manufacturers had given up trying to cope with Far Eastern pocket-portable competition or had simply capitulated and commissioned their own sets from there; radio sets with the Pye brand, a name famous in British receiver-manufacturing since the early 1920s, were made in Hong Kong for the first time in 1964. Radio had

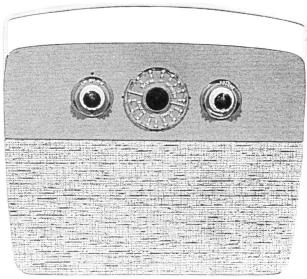

At a time when transistorised circuits were being widely employed in battery portables, the Ever Ready 'Sky Captain' of 1961 represented almost the last in a long line of valve portables stretching back to the 1920s. It has an unusual baffle front, covered in a two-tone check and pink 'Vynair' fabric, Vynair being the material widely favoured by Dansette record players of this period.

Electra Six Transistor pocket radio imported from Japan – an irresistible combination of black and ivory plastic and gilded metal! As a teenager, the author bought this little receiver from Dingles department store in Plymouth in February 1964. Unwrapping it from its presentation box on the top deck of the bus on the way home, he was severely warned by the conductor that he 'had better not switch that THING on up here!' This was well before the days of the Walkman and quality 'personal listening', although the tiny earpiece which came with the set was useful for secret under-the-pillow listening to the pirate radio stations or to Radio Luxembourg! The tinny sound produced by the minute loudspeaker of most Far Eastern pocket transistors was, by today's standards, appalling and has been described as being 'akin to an angry wasp in an empty milk bottle' (attributed to Gerry Wells, 1979).

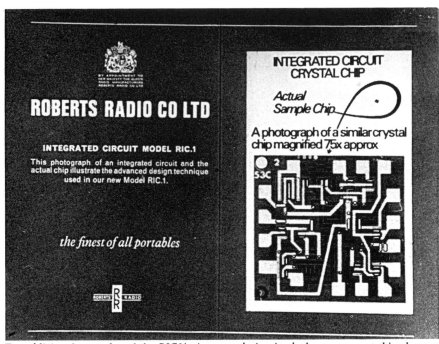

To publicise the novelty of the RIC1's integrated circuit, dealers were sent this showcard which had a sample of a reject microchip glued to it.

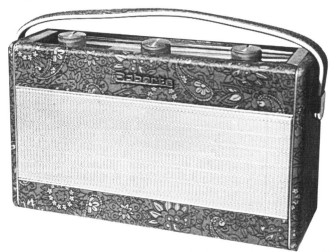

Another receiver which marks a very important development is the Roberts RIC1 of 1968. This was the first British-made radio to employ an integrated circuit (microchip). Reflecting the all-pervading influence of the 'hippy' period, this particular model was covered in a fashionable but non-standard yellow, orange and green paisley-patterned material, and in this form was available only from Harrods department store in London.

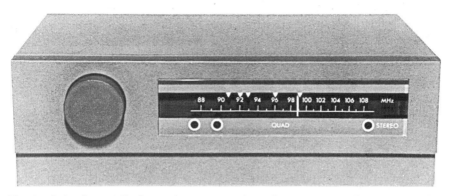

The simple but beautifully designed transistorised Quad FM3 Stereo Radio Tuner, manufactured by the Acoustical Manufacturing Company of Huntingdon in 1971. The increasing number of listeners were now demanding improved sound quality, a trend linked to the FM stereo transmissions from the BBC and, later, from other broadcasting companies.

become a secondary part of the industry, displaced by television as the centre of home entertainment, and now simply a useful provider of background music and background company. Radios that were still made in Britain were the larger transistor type, mains valve table models and valve or transistor hi-fi equipment. In this area, the BBC's first regular FM service in stereo was introduced in 1966, starting on the Third Programme and eventually spreading to all the BBC's main networks. Again, the introduction of a new service gave impetus to manufacturers, who were quick to produce quality stereo radios and tuners for this new market.

Transistor development had now led to the introduction of the integrated circuit (microchip) in which a large number of transistors, diodes and resistors could all be incorporated into a single tiny silicon chip. This did not necessarily mean that every radio using integrated circuitry became the size of a matchbox or smaller, for sound quality depended on the size of the loudspeaker and the case in which it was contained. Besides, as one commentator in *Practical Wireless* said, 'What's the point if a piece of equipment is smaller than the knob which is being used to control it?'.

A major reorganisation in broadcasting took place at 7.00 am on Saturday 30th September 1967 when the BBC's new all-pop music network, Radio 1, was inaugurated on 247 metres by the disc-jockey Tony Blackburn with his early-morning breakfast show. At the same time the BBC's other main networks, the Light, Third and Home Service, were given a new image and renamed Radio 2, Radio 3 and Radio 4 respectively. Listeners with older sets (there were now over 14 million licence holders) could send to the BBC for little stickers to go on their radio dials to show the positions of the new stations. A few years later, on 1st February 1971, the licence for receiving radio broadcasts was abolished and now only those with television sets had to purchase a licence.

After decades of valuable service to the radio and electronics industries, the valve had by the mid 1970s all but ceased being used in any form of electronic equipment. However, since the mid 1980s, there has been a dramatic resurgence in its use in specialist hi-fi amplifiers and tuners, and, while it seems unlikely that it will ever appear again in an ordinary domestic radio, this interest is a fitting tribute to a component that was first produced at the beginning of the twentieth century.

FURTHER READING

Hill, Jonathan. *Audio! Audio!* Sunrise Press, 1995. An illustrated directory of the valve audio amplifier, 96 A4 pages, 70+ photographs. Softback edition, signed. £12.50 including p&p from Sunrise Press, Spice House, 13 Belmont Road, Exeter, Devon EX1 2HF. Telephone: 01392 411565. Website: www.angelfire.com/tx/sunpress/index.html

Hill, Jonathan. *Radio! Radio!* Sunrise Press, 1996 (third edition). 'The Radio Collectors' Bible' – a profusely illustrated history of the British radio set from the late nineteenth century to the 1970s and beyond. 320 A4 pages, and 1000+ photographs. Signed and numbered hardback edition. £35 including p&p from Sunrise Press (address above).

Hill, Jonathan. *The Cat's Whisker, 50 Years of Wireless Design*. Oresko Books, London, 1978. An illustrated introduction to the history of wireless design up to the 1940s. Long out of print, but some libraries have copies in stock, and second-hand copies come to light from time to time.

CONTACTS AND USEFUL ADDRESSES

The British Vintage Wireless Society. Established in 1976, the BVWS holds regular radio swapmeets and auctions around Britain and publishes a quality quarterly magazine, newsletters with members' sales and wants and historical reprints of wireless catalogues and related publications. SAE c/o Sunrise Press (address above).

East Coast Wireless, 2 Holt Court, Walpole St Peter, Wisbech, Cambridgeshire PE14 7NY. Telephone: 01945 780808. Vintage wireless restoration, repairs and sales.

Len Kelly Books, 6 Redlands, Blundells Road, Tiverton, Devon EX16 4DH. Telephone: 01884 256170. Website: www.kellybooks.co.uk A mail-order specialist bookshop dealing in collectors' books and magazines (old and new) on vintage radio, television, audio etc. Catalogues regularly issued.

National Vintage Communications Fair. Held twice a year at the NEC in Birmingham, this huge and long established collectors' fair is supported by over 300 specialist dealers selling vintage radios, early televisions, telephones, gramophones, classic hi-fi, and all manner of electrical and mechanical antiques and collectables. Details from Sunrise Press (address above).

On The Air, The Vintage Technology Centre, The Highway, Hawarden, near Chester CH5 3DN. Telephone: 01244 530300. Website: www.vintageradio.co.uk A vintage sound shop that publishes a catalogue and newsletter.

Radio Bygones. Available by subscription from Wimborne Publishing Ltd, 408 Wimborne Road East, Ferndown, Dorset BH22 9ND. Telephone: 01202 873872. Website: www.radiobygones.com A vintage radio magazine covering domestic radio and television, broadcasting, amateur radio, military, aviation and marine communications etc. Published six times a year.

Savoy Hill Publications, Fir View, Rabys Row, Scorrier, Redruth, Cornwall TR16 5AW. Telephone: 01209 820771. Website: www.savoy-hill.co.uk Specialist supplier of circuit diagrams and other useful vintage radio, television and electronic service data. Publishes monthly newsletter.

PLACES TO VISIT

Intending visitors are advised to find out the days and the times of opening before making a special journey.

Amberley Museum, Amberley, Arundel, West Sussex BN18 9LT. Telephone: 01798 831370. Website: www.amberleymuseum.co.uk A comprehensive industrial archaeology museum, with a large radio section featuring a radio and television showroom of the 1950s.

Bognor Regis Wireless Museum, 69 High Street, Bognor Regis, West Sussex PO21 1RY. Telephone: 01243 865636.

How We Lived Then, Museum of Shops and Social History, 20 Cornfield Terrace, Eastbourne, East Sussex BN21 4NS. Telephone: 01323 737143.

Irish Radio Museum, Cork City Gaol, Convent Avenue, Sunday's Well, Cork City, Ireland. Telephone: (00353) 21 430 5022. Website: www.corkcitygaol.com

Montacute TV and Radio Museum, 1 South Street, Montacute, Somerset TA15 6XD. Telephone: 01935 823024.

National Vintage Wireless and Television Museum, The High Lighthouse, West Street, Harwich, Essex. Telephone: 07796 280980. Website: www.radiomiamigo.co.uk

Orkney Wireless Museum, Kiln Corner, Junction Road, Kirkwall, Orkney KW15 1LB. Telephone: 01856 871400. Website: www.owm.org.uk

Vintage Wireless Museum, 23 Rosendale Road, West Dulwich, London SE21 8DS. Telephone: 020 8670 3667. Colossal displays of vintage radios (pre- and post-war), plus expert repairs, spares and advice. Also runs Sunday workshops. Visits by appointment.

Wireless in the West, Tropiquaria, Washford Cross, near Watchet, West Somerset TA23 0JX. Telephone: 01984 640688. Website: www.tropiquaria.com An exhibition of radio broadcasting history housed in a former BBC transmitting station.